MW00669195

ACCEPTED!

A STEP BY STEP GUIDE
TO
COLLEGE ADMISSION

AAYC® College Planning Service
All About Your College
Dallas, Texas

Foreword

Congratulations on taking the first steps to understanding the process of college admission. This workbook, *ACCEPTED!*, is designed to guide the college bound student in public, private or home school. Experts once believed College Guidance began in the junior year. Later, they decided the student entering high school in 9th grade needed to have a general understanding of the process and what was at stake on the high school transcript. Now it is understood College Guidance really begins early in the junior high school years in order for the student to achieve advanced academic work offered in the junior and senior year of high school. However, one of the greatest lessons learned about the college process is it can be picked up at any time throughout any grade level and each student begins at their very own unique starting point in college planning.

Technology provides us with instant communication, rewards, and feedback. It's often difficult for parents and students to tackle the college admission process alone. At **ALL ABOUT YOUR COLLEGE (AAYC®)**, we believe you will find the *ACCEPTED!* workbook a helpful guide to take the steps necessary for your personal college admission. Remember, college admission is a process, not an event! The best news of all, the information provided in the **AAYC®** material is appropriate for parents and students in grades 7-12 in public, private, or home school who want information on understanding the college admission process. *ACCEPTED!* is a fundamental tool for you where ever you may be in this exciting process called college planning.

Colleges and universities throughout the United States are the envy of the world. A nationally honored counselor, Dr. Janet Miranda, has discovered there is typically not a "one and only" college for each student. Rather, there are probably five to ten wonderful schools where each student could thrive academically, socially and professionally. Just as people have personalities, so colleges have personalities as well. Our purpose is to guide you through the process to help you find colleges that match your personality, goals, and achievement. At **AAYC®** we are happy to model the way and become a part of this significant life process called college admission.

As a college admission specialist Dr. Miranda and **AAYC®** can not guarantee you admission to college. Each year is unique and it is impossible to have a crystal ball to see the credentials of the rest of the applicant pool for each class at each college. We can assure you this workbook is a process used by thousands of students to gain admission to their college and we want to help you in this important process. Let's get started as you prepare with your best effort for your personal college admission success.

"Chance favors a prepared mind!"
~Abraham Lincoln

AAYC® ALL ABOUT YOUR COLLEGE, LLC

ACCEPTED!

A College Planning Workbook from AAYC®

TABLE OF CONTENTS

ALL ABOUT YOUR COLLEGE
College Planning Workbook
Introduction

Statement of Philosophy

STUDENTS bring their talents, grade history, and testing results to the college decision table. Ultimately, the student will be the one attending classes, writing papers, and studying for exams all while networking and learning the roles of adult leadership. With parents, teachers, coaches, advisors, and counselors working with you as a team, it is now time for you, **THE STUDENT**, to take the lead and think about your future. This is a time when you, **THE STUDENT**, are encouraged to explore the many options set before you, realizing there is not one perfect plan but rather many potential opportunities awaiting you. Whether your background is from public school, private school or home school, you have your very own coaching staff. Your parents, siblings, family friends, teachers, and counselors make up your coaching staff but you, the applicant, are the captain of the team.

Testing is a critical **STEP ONE**. It's the only piece of the application comparing you to students across the nation. Once you know your testing range, **STEP TWO** is to discover and explore colleges appropriate for your personality, professional goals, and academic achievement. Armed with a list of schools, the **STEP THREE** in the process is the actual application. This workbook is designed to help you with all three of these key steps as well as **STEP FOUR** – discover scholarships and **STEP FIVE** – addresses special programs.

Who is Responsible?

The Student – Your college choice is one of your first major decisions in the process of taking charge of your adult professional life. If you do the paper work and you make the phone calls, you will feel confident when you step foot on campus. If your mother fills out your applications and your father makes all of the calls, you will find yourself clueless and embarrassed once you hit campus. Take advantage of all the people around you to "coach" you through this process but make sure that **YOU, the applicant,** make **ALL** contacts with each college. **Applicant is singular not plural!**

The Parent – The application process requires teamwork and parents are the head coaches of the team. However, parents are discouraged from contacting the college or university on behalf of the student. Parents often think they are helping the process or "opening doors" for the student. The fact is, when parents take over the process they are making **you**, the applicant, look incompetent. Parents often say, "But he/she is in school all day, they don't have time to call!" The reality is if you forget your lunch or leave your term paper on the kitchen counter, you would find time to call home. If contacting the college is important to you, there will be time for a phone call. Please don't let anyone rob you of the life learning experience gained when applying to college. The Dean of Admission at a most prestigious university, stated at a national conference, "If a parent calls me, I immediately think the student is too stupid to pick up the phone and dial ten numbers!" Enough said!

School Counselor – "The School Report" is completed by the person acting as your school counselor. Your school counselor should be your advocate. If you are home schooled you might consider working with a private counselor or work closely with a campus representative from each college where you plan to apply. A good high school counselor or college representative will make sure the college understands your school setting, i.e. college prep, home school, public, private, metropolitan, rural, etc. so that the admissions office can evaluate you in light of that setting. Get to know your school or college counselor so they can speak about you in a positive, knowledgeable way. The school counselor or private counselor should work for you with your best interest in mind, but cannot do so unless you have given him/her the "ammunition" needed—information and personal contact with you.

The College Representative – Students are encouraged to become well acquainted with the college representative. This is a person who works for the admissions office of at a particular college and is assigned to represent the college to you. This person will probably be the first reader of all applications from a particular high school, city, or area of the country. The identity of this person can be obtained easily by an inquiry to the admissions office or on the college website. Make every effort to get to know the college representative for your area, always remembering that their interest is in finding students who best match the college's interests and requirements.

Teachers – Some teachers are willing to write letters of recommendation but please realize teachers are not required to write letters of recommendation. It is NOT part of their job description nor do they get paid extra for taking time to do this task. It would be in YOUR best interest to demonstrate a work ethic worthy of a great letter of recommendation. Be a valuable contributor to the classroom setting. If you are home schooled, be diligent about your work. When requesting a letter of recommendation, think about who might have something positive to say about you and respectfully ask the instructor if they would be willing to write a letter for you. If the teacher agrees, give them a copy of your resume (see Step Three) and the proper teacher recommendation forms when required. Respect and thank you notes are a must even if you are home schooled. It's proper etiquette!

The High School Registrar – Transcripts must go from institution to institution. The school registrar will prepare and mail your transcript. Get to know this person at your school and be informed about the procedure for requesting a transcript. If you are home schooled, it is a good idea to present a structured, easy-to-read transcript indicating the subject, grade, credit earned, and the date of completion of each grading period.

Some colleges do not ask for recommendation letters; others may ask for as many as three. It is important to follow the directions for EACH college. Always give your recommendation writers and registrar a MINIMUM of ten working days notice when making a request for letters or transcripts.

My school counselor is _____

The school registrar is _____

Teachers I might want to write letters of recommendation are: *(If you are home schooled, think of people other than a parent who would be able to write about your academic work.)*

_____

_____

_____

_____

THE IMPORTANT ELEVATOR SPEECH

You may not have heard the terminology "Elevator Speech" but having a great one will immediately set you apart from many other admission candidates. An elevator speech is a 90 second statement you give to college representatives, your parents, aunts, uncles, grandparents – anyone who asks you where you want to go to college and what you want to study. A prepared "Elevator Speech" will make you sound brilliant compared to the student who stands there and responds, "I don't know." So, write your elevator speech in the space below to the question, "Where do you want to go to college and what do you think you might want to study?"

USE PENCIL – THIS IS LIKELY TO CHANGE!!!

I'm, looking at (name several colleges)_____

_____

_____

and I've thought about studying 1) _____;
2) _____**; 3)** _____

For I know the plans I have for you, to prosper you and not to harm you!
Jeremiah 29:11

"We are what we repeatedly do. Excellence, therefore, is not an act but a habit"
~Aristotle

Stay focused - Stay organized. Keep your notes together!
List the questions you need answered or things you need to consider:

_____

_____

_____

_____

_____

_____

_____

_____

_____

_____

_____

_____

_____

_____

SECTION ONE

-

TESTING

May you be strengthened with all power, according to his glorious might, for
all endurance and patience with joy.   Colossians 1:11

SECTION ONE
TESTING

Students often ask what is most important to college admission: grades, activities, or test scores? Think of those three essentials as the crucial legs of a three legged-stool. The stool can not stand with only two legs, **it takes all three**.   While all three, grades, activities and test scores must be present, the test score is the first consideration. Why? It's the only part of the admission puzzle comparing the student in Texas to the student in Utah or Missouri or Massachusetts. The school curriculum can be quite different from school to school and from state to state as can the ease or difficulty of obtaining a certain grade point average. Participation in activities will also produce vast differences. For large schools participation in a particular activity such as a varsity sport or student government can be limited to a few, and for students in small schools and those who are home schooled, the range of extra-curricular activities may be limited.   Thus, standardized test scores are the only national norm colleges have to compare students across the nation. Because the test score is critical, **AAYC**® considers testing as STEP ONE. As a college applicant, the test score will provide realistic college options for you.

PSAT (Preliminary SAT)

Because college testing is so important, two tests have been developed to help students prepare (practice) for the college entrance exams. The PSAT is administered on a national test date in October. Your school may test on a school day or you may be assigned to test on a Saturday. If you are home schooled, you may take the PSAT exam at the public school you would otherwise have attended in your area or you may be able to test at a nearby private school. Regardless of the actual day, the PSAT is a one-shot, one day test! The PSAT is the ONLY test to qualify for the **National Merit Scholarship Program**. Only the test taken in the junior year can be used to qualify. PSAT exams taken in the freshman and sophomore year are for practice. While the PSAT score is not required for college admission, your score will put you on desired mailing lists as a student worthy of attention. Many colleges subscribe to PSAT lists by group scores. Selective colleges may not receive your individual PSAT score, but they can request a mailing list from the testing company with the address for any student, for example, colleges can request names and addresses of students scoring higher than the SAT equivalent of a 1360 (old SAT score) or 2040 (new SAT score) on the PSAT. The colleges will not be able to determine your exact score identified with your name but they will know if you are within the testing range making you a viable candidate for their college.

NOTE: Check with your school counselor to determine the PSAT date for your school. Some schools automatically administer the exam to every student in certain grade levels; others test only the students who specifically register for it. You may need to register at your school for the exam. DO NOT MISS THIS EXAM YOUR JUNIOR YEAR and try to take a practice PSAT both your freshman and sophomore years!

If you are home schooled, you have two options: 1) take the PSAT at the public school you would normally attend; or 2) take the PSAT at a private school in your area. With either option, you will need to call in August and certainly no later than September 1st, reserve a test, and confirm the time testing is to begin on the testing date. Test materials are ordered late summer so it is important to confirm your space where you will take the PSAT.

A word about testing…You wouldn't think about playing a piano recital without practicing, performing a play without rehearsals, or sending an athletic team out for the big game without practicing. Why would you take the most important of tests, college entrance exams, without practicing?

You may have enough self-discipline to "practice" on your own by purchasing and working through several test prep books. A number of different companies produce these books. Each has its own particular style and format, costing in the range of $20-$30 each.

Many students benefit from a more structured environment for your test "practice". If you are one of these, think about taking an SAT or ACT prep class. Ask around to find out who provides the best prep service in your area.

The best prep class in my area is _____

The phone number is _____ *(What are you waiting for? Call! Get started!)*

YOUR NOTES AND SCHEDULE FOR COMPLETING TEST PREP:

I plan to take the SAT and/or ACT beginning on _____
(list the date)

Therefore, I know I need to begin my test prep at the ABSOLUTE latest date six months out. The date I need to begin is _____.

I have made arrangements to prep with _____

PLAN (Preliminary ACT)

The PLAN (formally the PACT) is the preliminary test for the ACT. This score is not part of a scholarship competition; however, it will offer valuable knowledge in planning for the SAT and ACT exams. The PLAN is designed to be a 10th grade test and the test results will provide information for you in determining if the ACT is the best exam for you to take for college admission. Check with your school counselor for the date of the PLAN examination at your school. If you are home schooled, check with your public school or private schools in your area to see if you can take the PLAN with them.

Now that you've completed your test prep and have taken the PSAT and the PLAN as practice, you are ready to take the tests the colleges will actually use to evaluate you.

SAT

Various colleges and universities require the Reasoning Test (SAT I), Subject Tests (SAT II), or ACT as part of their admission process. Many colleges waive the SAT Subject Tests if you take the ACT. **Carefully check your admission information from prospective colleges and universities to verify which tests and scores a particular college requires for admission.**

Think of the SAT and the ACT as two big department stores selling the same merchandise…try on the "outfits" from both stores and buy the one that looks best on you! Most colleges will accept either test.

Plan to complete ALL SAT Reasoning (SAT I) and ACT testing during your junior year! For testing dates and registration go to www.collegeboard.com and www.act.org

THE REASONING TEST (SAT I) – The Reasoning Test is a 5 hour test composed of multiple choice, fill-in-the-blank, essay, and writing questions. The results produce scores for three divisions: Critical Reading, Math, and Writing (a perfect score would equal 800 on each division with a possible 2400). Testing is offered ONLY seven times a year on Saturday mornings. Take a **MINIMUM** of two Reasoning Tests during the junior year. All colleges will take the highest test score on any given test date and many schools will split the scores (they call this super scoring) and take the highest essay, math or critical reading score from different test dates. As an applicant, it is your responsibility to know the testing requirements for the schools you plan to apply to and determine if the college or university will accept the best combination of scores or your highest test score on any one given test date. This policy can even change from year to year…ASK!

THE SUBJECT TESTS (formerly SAT II) - More selective colleges require the SAT subject tests as part of the admission process in addition to the Reasoning Test (SAT I) or ACT scores. Each subject test takes one hour to complete and you may take up to three (3) subjects on any given test day. It is important for you to know the SAT Reasoning and SAT Subjects are given on the same day so you can only take one or the other on a test day.

Plan your testing calendar carefully! To determine if your colleges require the SAT II Subject Tests, always check with the admission office at the college.

NOTE: Every college in the country will accept ACT or SAT scores for admission. If you score much higher on one exam over the other, submit only the test you want the college to see.

Many highly selective colleges are now accepting an ACT score in place of the Subject Test scores. For clarification, if you are applying to a college that requires Subject Test scores, ask if they will take an ACT exam in place of those scores. If you have a great ACT score and they will accept that score in place of Subject Tests…you're through testing. Submit your ACT and call it a day!

ACT – The ACT is a four hour test composed of an essay and four sections of multiple choice questions. The sections are: English; Math; Reading; Science Reasoning (logic) and Writing. When registering, the writing section is considered "optional". However, **DO TAKE THE WRITING PORTION at each ACT exam**. Each of the first four sections has a possible score of 36 and the four sections are averaged to provide a composite score. Some students perform better on the ACT and some find their best score on an SAT. Therefore, it is recommended to take both two SAT and two ACT exams in the spring of the junior year and then use the either the SAT or ACT exam that best represents your abilities and achievement to send to the colleges. An important difference to note is that the SAT Exam and the ACT Exam are given by two different companies, with two different policies with respect to sending test scores.

SENDING SCORES TO COLLEGES - A student can request that only one specific date's test score (the highest, of course) be sent from the ACT. Historically, SAT has been cumulative reporting – you take the exam two or three times and the colleges see all scores. However, beginning in March 2009, students may request SAT reports by one test date ONLY or a cumulative reporting. This may impact which test scores a student chooses to send. **NEVER** check the boxes to have scores sent for free **at the time** you take the test. **ALWAYS** wait until the fall of your senior year when you are completing your application to choose which scores to send to each college where you plan to apply.

Look at the web sites for both the College Board (SAT) (www.collegeboard.com) and ACT (www.act.org) to determine when the assessments are administered. The SAT is given seven times a year and the ACT six times a year. That's only 13 test dates in an entire academic year.

PLAN CAREFULLY and try to complete your required testing in your junior year! You will need to register for each test at least six weeks prior to the testing date when you plan to test. By registering early, you are more likely to get your first choice testing center, the cozy school down the street, rather than the huge unfamiliar high school across town.

SPECIAL ACCOMODATIONS

FOR LEARNING DIFFERENCES AND PHYSICAL DISABILITIES - If you need testing accommodations because of physical disabilities or learning differences, you will need to register for these special accommodations much further in advance. It typically takes a MINIMUM of six weeks to get approved for extended time and other accommodation. Requests may be denied, but if your request is legitimate, appeal the denial and demonstrate proof that you do require and deserve extended time. Look on the websites for more information regarding testing with special accommodations. You will need to complete special forms for these services.

NOTES ABOUT TESTING _____

_____

_____

_____

_____

_____

_____

_____

_____

_____

REGISTRATION: www.collegeboard.com   **Your CEEB Code** _____
                          www.act.org

You will need to know your high school code also referred to as the CEEB code. The school code is the same for both the SAT and ACT. To find your high school code for testing, use the following link:

    http://www.collegeboard.com/student/testing/sat/codelist.html

Home School codes are assigned by state. Additionally, you will need a credit card to register online.

WHEN ARE YOU TESTING?

Check your calendar and register NOW!
    Registered for SAT on _____
    Registered for SAT on _____
    Registered for ACT on _____
    Registered for ACT on _____

    Do you need to take SAT IIs? When?
    Registered for SAT II on _____
    Registered for SAT II on _____

OFFICIAL SCORES

Some colleges and universities require OFFICIAL test scores sent from SAT or ACT. While a college might accept a score from a high school transcript, with more and more computer generated transcripts, it is HIGHLY RECOMMEDED once you have achieved the scores you want the university to consider, you should send official scores to each college to which you plan to apply. Contact the College Board and/or ACT to have official scores sent.

        www.collegeboard.com   **www.act.org**

STANDBY TESTING

If you miss the late registration deadline, it is possible to take the test as a standby for a substantial fee. However, you will be allowed to test ONLY when all examinees who hold tickets for that specific center and examinees with center changes have been seated. **DO NOT RELY ON THIS OPTION.** There is no guarantee you will be able to test as a standby and the fees to test standby are substantial. **PLAN AHEAD** and register on time!

TEST PREPARATION WEBSITES

Test Prep
http://www.wisemantech.com/guidance/testprep.htm

SAT Reasoning and Subject Test Prep and Information
www.collegeboard.com

ACT Test Prep
www.actexampracticetests.com

"Perseverance is the hard work you do after you get tired of doing the hard work you already did!"
~ Newt Gingrich

Press on! It will be well worth your time in the end! You can find the SAT and ACT mid range of scores for particular colleges by completing a college search (See SECTION TWO). Researching colleges will give you a goal for your test preparation and will inform you which colleges normally accept students with scores in your testing range.

SAT and ACT Test-taking Strategies

SAT – The SAT is scored giving you one point for every correct answer, zero points for every question not answered, and will deduct a fraction of a point for every question answered incorrectly. It is still a better strategy to guess on a question rather than leaving it blank if you can eliminate at least one of the answer choices as being wrong. With test prep, you will probably find that you can eliminate one or two of the answer choices on almost every question.

Early in the set of questions, the obvious answer is usually right. Questions on each section usually proceed from easiest to more difficult. Later in the set on the more difficult questions, the obvious answers are usually wrong. Later in the set, you can usually eliminate the more obvious choice if you are guessing.

Look for the fast points in Critical Reading. If you are short on time and can't read every passage, try to answer the "Vocabulary in Context" questions. These questions have a line reference you can refer back to without reading the entire passage.

ACT - Always guess on the ACT. No points will be deducted for incorrect answers.

On the ACT, the answer is often hidden in some way. Study the answer choices carefully. It might be written in a way that students don't expect – such as .5 instead of ½ .

REMEMBER THE 1/3 RULE

Remember, you are encouraged to take a MINIMUM of two SATs and two ACTs. Most colleges will accept either test. Of all students who take both tests, one-third do better on ACT, one-third do better on SAT and one-third do about the same on both.

ON THE DAY OF THE TEST

BE ON TIME and bring the following with you to the test center:
1) admission ticket
2) **photo I.D.**
3) several #2 pencils
4) eraser
5) calculator with fresh batteries
6) snacks (for the break to give you extra energy as the test goes on)
7) dress in layers as the room temperature will vary. You could be in a room that is sweltering or you may need a sweater.
8) **DO NOT ARRIVE LATE. YOU WILL NOT BE SEATED IF TESTING HAS BEGUN.**

Comparison SAT/ACT*

5 sections
M,R,W,E,Sc

3 sections
800 800 800
M   R   W
(500)

guessing penalty

ACT	OLD SAT Cr + M ONLY	NEW SAT
36	1600	2400
35	1540-1590	2340
34	1490-1530	2260
33	1440-1480	2190
32	1400-1430	2130
31	1360-1390	2040
30	1330-1350	1980
29	1290-1320	1920
28	1250-1280	1860
27	1210-1240	1820
26	1170-1200	1760
25	1130-1160	1700
24	1090-1120	1650
23	1050-1080	1590
22	1020-1040	1530
21	980-1010	1500
20	940-970	1410

Many colleges are still trying to decide how they will evaluate the essay component of both the SAT and ACT. Many schools still determine entrance based solely on the verbal (critical reading) and math of the SAT or the four sections making up the composite score of the ACT. You may find the above chart helpful in evaluating your scores.

While colleges may not use the essay portion of the exam as part of your initial evaluation, they still want to see the essay results. **Take the essay on both the SAT and ACT seriously!** Some colleges will compare this essay with those on your application. Colleges are looking for proof that a student can write at a level that will allow him/her to step up to college level work. Every essay is important!

NOTE: This chart was not created by nor endorsed by ACT or the College Board.

While you're thinking about testing…here's some quick information regarding Advanced Placement testing. Many students enrolled in AP® classes take AP tests each May. Colleges will treat these scores in different ways: some will grant college credit for certain scores, others will not grant credit but will admit the student to a higher level of class (sometimes avoiding large sections of freshman-level classes), while others merely use the scores as proof of college readiness. "Required" scores can differ for majors within a large university and the most selective schools typically do not grant AP credit even with a score of 5 (AP tests are scored on a 1 to 5 scale with 5 being the highest). Please check with your college BEFORE you sign up for exams to determine your testing options. On the other hand, every college wants to see that you are enrolled in AP courses and taking the most rigorous curriculum available to you. Carefully evaluate your own strategy for taking or not taking AP exams.

NOTES AND COLLEGE PLANNING IDEAS:

_____

_____

_____

_____

_____

_____

_____

_____

_____

_____

_____

_____

_____

_____

_____

SECTION TWO
-
RESEARCHING COLLEGE OPTIONS

SECTION TWO
RESEARCHING COLLEGE OPTIONS

Once you know your realistic test score range, it's time to shop for colleges. What do you want to study? Where do you want to live? Small school vs. large university? Activities? Campus Life? The Internet provides a plethora of information in the process of selecting a college. To begin your college search let's try to identify your goals, wants and needs. Here are some questions that you may want to ask yourself before you begin your college search.

I'd like to study...

_____

_____

_____

Because...

_____

_____

_____

_____

I prefer to be in: (circle one)

Metropolitan area   Medium city   Suburb

Rural area   Location doesn't matter

Because...

_____

_____

Consider your personal goals and how to reach them...
- Are you a self starter? _____
- Will it make a difference if no one cares if you attend class? _____
- Do you work best if someone motivates you? _____

Circle all that apply: I would like to attend college in:

Northeast	Southeast	Midwest
Texas	Northwest	Southwest
California	location is not important to me	

Circle one: I would enjoy a campus with about:

20,000+ students;   15,000 to 20,000 students;   10,000 to 15,000 students;

5,000 to 10,000 students;   less than 5,000 students.

College activities important to me include:
(for example – music, athletics, visual arts, drama, etc.)

_____

_____

_____

_____

Great sources to use for college searches are:

College Board
www.collegeboard.com/student

Fast Web
www.fastweb.com

**ALWAYS CHECK THE WEBSITE OF AN INDIVIDUAL
COLLEGE FOR THE MOST CURRENT INFORMATION.**

DISCOVERING A COLLEGE

Searching the web or visiting with a representative from the school is usually the first step to gaining insight into a college. Another valuable source of information is to visit with someone who is a current student on campus. Ask friends and family if they know anyone who attends the colleges you would like to learn more about.

Printed college guides can also be a good source of information because they compare various colleges. Understand that each guidebook has its own point of view and biases. Never take the word of only one source of information. Absolutely nothing takes the place of actually visiting the campus. Begin your campus visits with a college close to home or perhaps even in your city. DO NOT MAKE YOUR VERY FIRST CAMPUS VISIT TO WHAT YOU THINK IS YOUR FIRST CHOICE COLLEGE. Learn the ropes and observe what people say and do on college visits…you'll learn what TO DO as well as what NOT TO DO by watching others on your first campus visit.

COLLEGE FAIRS

Check with your counselor and local news media (radio, TV, newspaper) to determine the dates and times of college fairs in your area. Most likely, the representative attending your fair will be the "First Read" on applications received from your school and/or area of the country.

When you attend a College fair program, walk up to the table and greet the college representative looking him/her in the eye and shaking his/her hand as you introduce yourself. **State your name and the school you attend.**

Be prepared to ask three to five specific questions and gather information. Always pick up the business card of the person representing the college.

ACT INTERESTED – even if you're not…be courteous!

After the fair, send a note of thanks to the representatives from schools of interest to you.

* Make sure you have your "Elevator Speech" ready before you go to your college fair. (see vii)

QUESTIONS TO ASK A COLLEGE REP

Three BIG ones…

1. How many applicants and what percent are accepted? This will tell you where you are in the total applicant pool.

2. What percent of first year students return as sophomores? You will discover if the students are happy, do they like the school, and whether the admissions office is doing a good job choosing students who are well-suited to the school.

3. What percent of entering students actually graduate IN FOUR YEARS? This is the reason to go to college, right? You do want a degree, right? You might be surprised how many students attend college for several years, spending a great deal of money, never to complete their degree.

And more…

4. What are your most popular programs?

5. Do you require additional applications for scholarships?

6. What is your average class size? How big is your largest class?

7. What is the most pressing issue on your campus right now?

8. What's the best thing about your school?

9. Do you offer…(a particular major/sport/activity)…

Ask something specific about each individual university – let them know you have at least taken the initiative to find out some things about their respective colleges.
- *I saw on your website…*
- *I read in your materials…*
- *I've heard that…*

COLLEGE FAIRS AND CAMPUS VISITS = FAMILY TIME

It may sound like fun to go to college fairs or campus visits with friends, but this is RARELY a good idea. Most likely you and even your best friends will have very different goals for your academic preparation to ultimately achieve your professional goals. If your best friend is less than attentive it could actually end up leaving the college with a negative impression of you. This is a FAMILY experience between the applicant (notice this is singular) and parents, who are the coaches and bankers for the applicant!

Now might be a great time to take inventory and actually state your thoughts and goals on the college process.

Why do you want to go to college? _____

_____

_____

Rarely will you find a one and only perfect college. **Shop!** Make sure you have a good fit before you buy the package! Develop a list of five (5) to ten (10) colleges you'd most like to consider. *USE PENCIL…THIS LIST WILL CHANGE!*

1. _____

2. _____

3. _____

4. _____

5. _____

6. _____

7. _____

8. _____

9. _____

10. _____

Initially, you can work from this list, but the list should evolve as you learn more about colleges and universities and are able to recognize more specifically what you are finally looking for to pursue your education. The college list is "organic!" You will need to devote time for growing and pruning!

VISITING CAMPUS

"You gotta go to know!" Visiting campus for a few hours will tell you much about the college and your fit for the university. Everyone has a "comfort zone" when it comes to people, places, and things. College visitation days are an important part of the process. Ideally, you will want to visit colleges during your sophomore and junior year of high school. Try to visit when school is in session. You'll get a much more accurate picture of the school. It would be a bad surprise to choose a school because of buildings only to show up on campus and find fellow students who don't fit your expectations.

Early spring of the juniors year or fall of the senior year are great times to visit a college campus. Check with the admissions office of schools you are seriously considering to inquire if they run any special visitation programs. You'll get to see much more if you attend one of these special visitation programs.

BEFORE THE CAMPUS VISIT

To schedule your visit, YOU, the student, the applicant, should contact the office of admission on campus at least two weeks before the planned visit. **Request to visit a class or specific department of interest to you.** A tour of the campus does not necessarily include visiting a class so ask for it! When you check in with the receptionist, politely confirm your desire and previous request to visit a class as well as take the tour.

.
Prep before you go to get the most out of your campus visit!

- Use the computer to study up on the campus and have a general understanding of the requirements for admission.

- Make a list of the things that impress you from the website as well as the things you have doubts about. After the visit this list can be used to verify if your initial impressions were accurate.

- Maps and parking info are available from the campus website.

- **BE ON TIME!**

- If you plan to play intercollegiate athletics or participate in a performing ensemble, try to meet with the coach or director during your campus visit.

- It is difficult to make more than one thorough campus visit per day. It is possible to do two if the campuses are very close together, however, only one is recommended.

Discover the "HANG OUT". Before you leave the campus, find out where the students "hang out". Frequently, although not always, this is at the Student Union or Student Commons. Go there and sit and watch for thirty minutes to an hour. Do the students look like you? Do they act like you? How do they treat each other? Are they carrying books? Do they look happy? Do you see yourself there? Why or why not? Write down the answers to these questions while it's fresh. You think you will always remember, but if you are visiting several campuses you need to record your impressions before the visits run together! Write your "thank you" notes immediately after the visit when your thoughts will be fresh and you can mention something specific about the campus. These "thank you" notes will cause people in the admissions office to remember you in a positive way.

Read the bulletin boards! You'll find out what really goes on around campus if you'll take the time to read the bulletin boards. Take a close look at the activities advertised on the boards. Do you see yourself going to these events?

WHAT TO LOOK FOR ON A TOUR
(It's a lot to juggle!)

1. General appearance of the campus (poor maintenance/ vandalism/campus pride)

2. Student attire (Do they look like you? Is it a "jeans and T-shirt" campus or "khaki and polo" campus?)

3. Friendliness (eye contact/offer to help)

4. Student conversations (topic/tone/classes/papers/books/parties)

5. Transportation (to and from the school as well as around the campus)

6. Faculty presence (office hours posted/open doors/student interaction)

7. Library, laboratory and computing facilities (Hours? Easy access? How crowded are the different facilities?)

8. Fine arts facilities (studios/practice rooms/performance centers)

9. Dorms (wired/secure/coed or single sex/substance free)

10. CAMPUS SECURITY – what is the crime rate? How serious?

On the tour, talk to students and ask…

- Do students stay on campus on the week end?
- How many hours a week do you study?
- Do you study in the dorm or library…or some other place?
- Is it easy to get the classes you want to take?
- How many classes do you have that are taught by full professors?
- Is it easy to get additional help if you need it?
- What do you like the most about this college?
- What was your biggest surprise good or bad when you got here?

Visiting a Class…

When you visit a campus, ask to visit a class. If you don't ask for this and set it up ahead of time you will only get the campus tour. Observe…

- Are the students engaged?
- Does class begin on time?
- Does the professor seem prepared?
- Is it lecture or Socratic (open discussion)?
- Ask yourself if you would be challenged by this class.
- Do the students seem engaged in learning?

The voyage of discovery is not in seeking new landscapes…but in having new eyes.
~Marcel Proust

Other Things You Might Want to Know…

What percent of graduates who apply to law school are admitted? Med school?
MBA programs?

What percent of **first year or core curriculum** classes are taught by graduate students (often called "TA's" for Teaching Assistants)?

Ask your tour guide what made them choose the school and if they were looking again, would they still choose the same school. Look for facial expressions and any hesitation in their voice.

Ask the tour guide what has made the biggest impression on them at the school…and what was their biggest surprise when they got to the school?

Find out from professors about internships in your major field of study. What three companies recruit the majority of graduates in your field from the college?

Proper Etiquette – Don't Forget Your Manners!

When you meet a college rep at a fair or school visitation, pick up a business card and write a personal note. It doesn't need to be long…just the facts. Few people take the time to write a "thank you". If you do, they will remember you!

Dear *(name of the rep)*,

    Thank you so much for coming to the college fair at *(location)*. I really appreciated learning more about *(the name of the college)*.

               Yours truly,

               Chris Applicant

Mannerly gestures such as writing a personal note can carry you a long way in life! Welcome to the real world! An email response to the rep may get deleted, but a personal note will go in your file.

START STRONG…FINISH STRONG!

VISITING WITH A PURPOSE
COLLEGE VISIT CHECKLIST

When visiting a college, go with a check list…a purpose…know what you want to find and see if it's there. This is a generic college visit template. You may use this one or create one specific to you and what you most hope to find on a college visit. Use the same template for each campus you visit for the best comparison of schools.

College _____

Address of the School _____

Appointment Date and Time _____

Admission Contact _____

Ratings: 1 = poor   5 = excellent

ACADEMICS

Strength of academic programs	1	2	3	4	5
Size of class	1	2	3	4	5
Level of overall academic challenge	1	2	3	4	5
Quality of faculty	1	2	3	4	5
Support services (tutoring, counseling, career placement)	1	2	3	4	5

____TOTAL POINTS

NOTES:

CAMPUS LIFE

Residence halls	1	2	3	4	5
Food	1	2	3	4	5
Safety	1	2	3	4	5
Transportation	1	2	3	4	5

____ TOTAL POINTS

NOTES:

CAMPUS ACTIVITIES

Social organizations	1	2	3	4	5
Sports	1	2	3	4	5
Opportunities for music and theater	1	2	3	4	5
Religious organizations	1	2	3	4	5
Off-campus attractions	1	2	3	4	5

_____ TOTAL POINTS

NOTES:

CAMPUS APPEAL

First impression	1	2	3	4	5
Classrooms	1	2	3	4	5
Residence halls	1	2	3	4	5
Dining hall	1	2	3	4	5
Student Center	1	2	3	4	5
Appearance of the students	1	2	3	4	5
Library	1	2	3	4	5
Technology	1	2	3	4	5

_____ TOTAL POINTS

NOTES:

_____ GRAND TOTAL

Do you see yourself on this campus?	_____ Yes	_____ No
Do you see people you'd like to have as friends?	_____ Yes	_____ No
Did you meet professors you'd like to study with?	_____ Yes	_____ No

If you can't answer yes to all three…find another school!

VISITING WITH A PURPOSE
COLLEGE VISIT CHECKLIST

(Additional Copy)
Use the same template for each campus you visit for the best comparison of schools.

College _____

Address of the School _____

Appointment Date and Time _____

Admission Contact _____

Ratings: 1 = poor   5 = excellent

ACADEMICS

Strength of academic programs	1	2	3	4	5
Size of class	1	2	3	4	5
Level of overall academic challenge	1	2	3	4	5
Quality of faculty	1	2	3	4	5
Support services (tutoring, counseling, career placement)	1	2	3	4	5

____TOTAL POINTS

NOTES:

CAMPUS LIFE

Residence halls	1	2	3	4	5
Food	1	2	3	4	5
Safety	1	2	3	4	5
Transportation	1	2	3	4	5

____ TOTAL POINTS

NOTES:

CAMPUS ACTIVITIES

Social organizations	1	2	3	4	5
Sports	1	2	3	4	5
Opportunities for music and theater	1	2	3	4	5
Religious organizations	1	2	3	4	5
Off-campus attractions	1	2	3	4	5

_____ **TOTAL POINTS**

NOTES:

CAMPUS APPEAL

First impression	1	2	3	4	5
Classrooms	1	2	3	4	5
Residence halls	1	2	3	4	5
Dining hall	1	2	3	4	5
Student Center	1	2	3	4	5
Appearance of the students	1	2	3	4	5
Library	1	2	3	4	5
Technology	1	2	3	4	5

_____ **TOTAL POINTS**

NOTES:

_____ **GRAND TOTAL**

Do you see yourself on this campus?	_____ Yes	_____ No
Do you see people you'd like to have as friends?	_____ Yes	_____ No
Did you meet professors you'd like to study with?	_____ Yes	_____ No

If you can't answer yes to all three…find another school!

VISITING WITH A PURPOSE
COLLEGE VISIT CHECKLIST

(Additional Copy)
Use the same template for each campus you visit for the best comparison of schools.

College _____

Address of the School _____

Appointment Date and Time _____

Admission Contact _____

Ratings: 1 = poor   5 = excellent

ACADEMICS

Strength of academic programs	1 2 3 4 5	
Size of class	1 2 3 4 5	
Level of overall academic challenge	1 2 3 4 5	
Quality of faculty	1 2 3 4 5	
Support services (tutoring, counseling, career placement)	1 2 3 4 5	

____TOTAL POINTS

NOTES:

CAMPUS LIFE

Residence halls	1 2 3 4 5	
Food	1 2 3 4 5	
Safety	1 2 3 4 5	
Transportation	1 2 3 4 5	

____ TOTAL POINTS

NOTES:

28

CAMPUS ACTIVITIES

Social organizations	1	2	3	4	5
Sports	1	2	3	4	5
Opportunities for music and theater	1	2	3	4	5
Religious organizations	1	2	3	4	5
Off-campus attractions	1	2	3	4	5

_____ **TOTAL POINTS**

NOTES:

CAMPUS APPEAL

First impression	1	2	3	4	5
Classrooms	1	2	3	4	5
Residence halls	1	2	3	4	5
Dining hall	1	2	3	4	5
Student Center	1	2	3	4	5
Appearance of the students	1	2	3	4	5
Library	1	2	3	4	5
Technology	1	2	3	4	5

_____ **TOTAL POINTS**

NOTES:

_____ **GRAND TOTAL**

Do you see yourself on this campus?	_____ Yes	_____ No
Do you see people you'd like to have as friends?	_____ Yes	_____ No
Did you meet professors you'd like to study with?	_____ Yes	_____ No

If you can't answer yes to all three…find another school!

VISITING WITH A PURPOSE
COLLEGE VISIT CHECKLIST

(Additional Copy)
Use the same template for each campus you visit for the best comparison of schools.

College _____

Address of the School _____

Appointment Date and Time _____

Admission Contact _____

Ratings: 1 = poor   5 = excellent

ACADEMICS

Strength of academic programs	1	2	3	4	5
Size of class	1	2	3	4	5
Level of overall academic challenge	1	2	3	4	5
Quality of faculty	1	2	3	4	5
Support services (tutoring, counseling, career placement)	1	2	3	4	5

____TOTAL POINTS

NOTES:

CAMPUS LIFE

Residence halls	1	2	3	4	5
Food	1	2	3	4	5
Safety	1	2	3	4	5
Transportation	1	2	3	4	5

____ TOTAL POINTS

NOTES:

CAMPUS ACTIVITIES

Social organizations	1	2	3	4	5
Sports	1	2	3	4	5
Opportunities for music and theater	1	2	3	4	5
Religious organizations	1	2	3	4	5
Off-campus attractions	1	2	3	4	5

_____ **TOTAL POINTS**

NOTES:

CAMPUS APPEAL

First impression	1	2	3	4	5
Classrooms	1	2	3	4	5
Residence halls	1	2	3	4	5
Dining hall	1	2	3	4	5
Student Center	1	2	3	4	5
Appearance of the students	1	2	3	4	5
Library	1	2	3	4	5
Technology	1	2	3	4	5

_____ **TOTAL POINTS**

NOTES:

_____ **GRAND TOTAL**

Do you see yourself on this campus?	_____ Yes	_____ No
Do you see people you'd like to have as friends?	_____ Yes	_____ No
Did you meet professors you'd like to study with?	_____ Yes	_____ No

If you can't answer yes to all three...find another school!

VISITING WITH A PURPOSE
COLLEGE VISIT CHECKLIST

(Additional Copy)
Use the same template for each campus you visit for the best comparison of schools.

College _____

Address of the School _____

Appointment Date and Time _____

Admission Contact _____

Ratings: 1 = poor   5 = excellent

ACADEMICS

Strength of academic programs	1	2	3	4	5
Size of class	1	2	3	4	5
Level of overall academic challenge	1	2	3	4	5
Quality of faculty	1	2	3	4	5
Support services (tutoring, counseling, career placement)	1	2	3	4	5

____TOTAL POINTS

NOTES:

CAMPUS LIFE

Residence halls	1	2	3	4	5
Food	1	2	3	4	5
Safety	1	2	3	4	5
Transportation	1	2	3	4	5

____ TOTAL POINTS

NOTES:

CAMPUS ACTIVITIES

Social organizations	1	2	3	4	5
Sports	1	2	3	4	5
Opportunities for music and theater	1	2	3	4	5
Religious organizations	1	2	3	4	5
Off-campus attractions	1	2	3	4	5

____ **TOTAL POINTS**

NOTES:

CAMPUS APPEAL

First impression	1	2	3	4	5
Classrooms	1	2	3	4	5
Residence halls	1	2	3	4	5
Dining hall	1	2	3	4	5
Student Center	1	2	3	4	5
Appearance of the students	1	2	3	4	5
Library	1	2	3	4	5
Technology	1	2	3	4	5

____ **TOTAL POINTS**

NOTES:

____ **GRAND TOTAL**

Do you see yourself on this campus?	____ Yes	____ No
Do you see people you'd like to have as friends?	____ Yes	____ No
Did you meet professors you'd like to study with?	____ Yes	____ No

If you can't answer yes to all three…find another school!

Notes from College Fairs and College Visits

TIPS FOR INTERVIEWS

Realize you are ALWAYS interviewing, albeit informally, every time you speak or meet with anyone representing the college. If the college is far from your state, and they require an interview, you may be asked to have your interview while making a campus visit. If not on campus, a local alumni professional in your city may interview you. A resume (STEP THREE) multi-tasks for you: it gives the interviewer an easy "jumping off point" for conversation, provides a place for him/her to take notes, and serves as a physical reminder when he/she is later thinking about you. Here are some tips for successful interviews.

1. Bring a copy of your resume. Don't assume that the interviewer has one.
2. Dress neatly but like a kid! Dress is a sign of your respect for the interviewer and the process.
3. Arrive promptly but not early and certainly NOT LATE!
4. Be prepared. Do your research on the college before you arrive so that you can ask informed, intelligent questions about this particular college.
5. Directly answer the question asked by the interviewer,
6. Show self-confidence with a firm handshake and good eye contact.
7. Converse! Be engaging! An interview is a two-way conversation. Be prepared to hold up your end of the conversation but also ask about the interviewer's experiences at the college.
8. Take advantage of the opportunity to discuss issues, activities, or goals you may not have presented in your application.
9. Leave the interviewer with the impression that you are engaging, positive, and specifically interested in _that_ school. No one wants to recommend someone dull or negative or who has not shown a particular reason to be attracted to the school.
10. Never chew gum. Never lie. Never answer just "yes" or "no".

QUESTIONS FROM ACTUAL COLLEGE INTERVIEWS

Why are you interested in our college?

What book(s) have you read this year that were not required reading for school?

> _Answer this question honestly. Few high school students read "War and Peace" in their spare time, but interviewers want to know why you were interested in what ever outside reading you did._

Describe yourself to someone who does not know you. Be truthful but POSITIVE. This may also come as describe yourself with three adjectives..."honest, responsible, hard working" – are all overused...use a thesaurus; or the question might be describe yourself to a future roommate (humor is good!).

How have you prepared yourself for college?

What experience has made you feel most alive?

If you could amend any part of the constitution what would it be and why?

Tell me about two of your best friends.

What academic areas most interest you? Why?

How have you spent your summers?

What would you change about your school?

What is your favorite class at school? What class has impacted your life?

What extra-curricular activities brought you the most satisfaction? Why?

How do you spend your free time during the school year?

What has been the greatest personal challenge in your life?

Who are your heroes/heroines?

Why do you believe you're a good candidate for our college?

What courses are you taking in your senior year?

What is your worst fault that might make you stumble in college and professional life?

You are very accomplished but out of all of your activities what is the one thing that best exemplifies your leadership?

Tell me about something you have had to overcome and what have you learned from it?

If you suddenly became rich, what would you do with the money?

What extra curricular activity has been the most satisfying and why?

Who is your favorite author?

If you could do high school over again, what would you do differently?

What's the most creative thing you've done?

What would your friends say about you?

What one thing would you like for me to tell the admissions committee in my report to them?

Be engaging! Maintain eye contact. Ask the interviewer why they chose the college. Ask them what their biggest surprise was once they arrived on campus.

THANK YOU NOTES

Always write a note to anyone who interviews you. *In the space below, draft your thank you note to the person who interviewed you. This note needs to be a bit longer, recalling something of significance the interviewer said to you and reiterating your sincere interest in the school.*

"…not the will to win…It's the will to PREPARE to win! Everyone has the will to win; few have the will to prepare!" ~Vince Lombardi

NOTES ON CAMPUS VISITS AND INTERVIEWS

College _____ **Interviewed by** _____

Notes: _____

_____

_____

College _____ **Interviewed by** _____

Notes: _____

_____

_____

College _____ **Interviewed by** _____

Notes: _____

_____

_____

NOTES ON CAMPUS VISITS AND INTERVIEWS (add'l)

College _____ **Interviewed by** _____

Notes:_____

_____

_____

College _____ **Interviewed by** _____

Notes:_____

_____

_____

College _____ **Interviewed by** _____

Notes:_____

_____

_____

College _____ **Interviewed by** _____

Notes:_____

_____

_____

College _____ **Interviewed by** _____

Notes:_____

_____

_____

SECTION THREE

-

RESUMES & APPLICATIONS

SECTION THREE
RESUMES & APPLICATIONS

It's time to take a self-evaluation. A resume is a great way to give your reader (the admission rep reading your application) an overview of your grades, test scores, activities, travel, church work, and community service. Include ALL **leadership** positions. Your list of activities may also indicate frequency and duration of your involvement. Good resumes take many forms, but they must be easy to understand without great effort from the reader. Limit it to your most important activities that will fit easily with legible font size on one neat and orderly page. Think of the resume as a marketing tool for you! If your activity is a universal one such as National Honor Society, you do not need to provide more information. If the activity is unique to YOU or your school, provide additional information, such as "Mission Trip – built orphanage in Mexico" or "Piano Soloist – placed in the top three at state level competition – 9, 10, 11".

USA SUPER STUDENT
1000 University Drive
Collegetown, USA 12345
123-456-7890
Email:

GPA: 4.45 (include ONLY if GPA is 3.5 and above)
RANK: 4/100 (include ONLY if rank is in the top 25%)

ACTIVITIES	Hrs wk/Wks yr
Varsity Soccer – 9, 10, 11, 12	10/14
All District – 11	
State Champions – 10, 11	
Band – 9, 10, 11, 12	8/32
Student Director – 11, 12	
Drama Productions – 9, 10, 11, 12	6/12
Male Lead – 10 Oklahoma, 11-The Fantasticks	
Student Government – 9, 10, 11	2/32
Class Representatives – 9	
Class President – 10, 11	

HONORS
Citizenship Award – 9, 10, 11 (awarded to one boy/one girl per grade)
National Honor Society – 10, 11, 12
   Vice President – 12 (responsible for 8 assembly programs including initiation)
Community Service Award – 10, 11 (30+ hours/year)
Presidential Classroom – Washington D.C. – 11 (week long classes & seminars)
West Point Summer Program – 11 (highly selective program for leadership & grades)

COMMUNITY
Certified Red Cross Lifesaving and CPR
Meals on Wheels volunteer – (summer 9, 10, 11) 6/12
Church Youth Group Student Leader – 11, 12   4/52
   (responsible for planning programs, budget, and reporting to Church Council)
Mexico Mission Trip – 11, 12 (Team leader of 12/building & repairing buildings)

EMPLOYMENT
Tom Thumb Grocery Store (customer service)   10/40
Presbyterian Hospital – 12 (Assisted nursing staff)   10/21

HIGH QUALITY APPLICATONS
ARE NOT COMPLETED AT ONE SITTING!

The application is a process not an event! …and the process will take several hours and several sessions over a period of time if you want to present your best possible work. If you submit your first draft, it will scream "first draft – no extra effort!"

SUBMIT ONLINE!

You have more control over the application if you submit it online. If you send the college a hard copy, you will be at the mercy of someone at the university (usually a work/study student) to enter your data for you.

Some students like to print out a hard copy of the application, fill it in, then, transfer the data to an online application for submission. **ALWAYS print yourself a copy to proof and to keep before you push *"submit"* sending the application to the university.** Submit your applications early in the "admissions season". If you wait until the last minute, it says to the colleges "I'm not organized!" Additionally, some university computer servers will become overloaded during the last several days before a deadline, preventing some applications from even being submitted.

Always obtain confirmation from the school that your electronically submitted application has been received. If they email confirmation to you, print out the email and keep it. If they don't, follow up with a polite phone inquiry and ask for email confirmation. Keep a record of the date of the call and the name of the person you talked to every time you call the college.

THE COMMON APPLICATION

Many private colleges and a few state colleges accept the Common Application. www.commonapp.org

The Associate Dean of Admission at a prestigious highly selective state school in the northeast remarked that she thought every junior should complete a Common Application, including the essays and then place it in a folder for later use. She then laughed and said her university didn't even accept the Common Application. Why would she make such a statement and encourage students to complete a Common Application? Her point was, there are only so many questions that can possibly be asked on any application and if you have one completed draft copy ready to go, you will most likely have all of the information you need to complete any other college application – organized in one folder, in one place!

When possible, you are encouraged to use the Common Application forms. If a college subscribes to the Common Application, they really don't care if you use the Common Application instead of their own application. Some schools don't even print their own application anymore.

More selective schools will require supplements to the Common Application. If you go to the Common Application website, not only will you see the extensive list of schools which accept the Common Application, you can find any required supplements at this site as well. Some supplements can be completed electronically; others must be submitted by hard copy. Anytime you send **anything** hard copy to the college, use your resume as the cover sheet and be sure your name and identification are on every page. Admission offices receive a lot of paper. You want to identify YOUR papers for YOUR file!

APPLICATIONS FOR STATE SCHOOLS

Many of the more populous states such as Texas and California have a common application for their respective state colleges and universities. When a common application for your state is available, by all means use it. Like some privates, many state colleges don't even print their own applications and require the applicant to use the common application for that state. It is easier for them and often easier for you as well.

WHEN A COMMON APPLICATION IS NOT AVAILABLE

If a particular school does not subscribe to a common application, either private or state, you will be required to complete the individual institution application. Check the website for the college to download the application and print your working copy (draft) or begin completing the online application. Almost every college will offer the option to complete the application online.

SNAIL MAIL

If you must mail a hard copy to a college or university, make a copy to keep for your records and send the application through the U.S. Postal Service, Priority Mail with delivery confirmation. That way, you will know that the materials were received. Send AT LEAST SEVEN WORKING DAYS BEFORE THE DUE DATE to allow for mail irregularities (but then you'll be completing these applications long before they're due, right?)! **If you're just meeting the application deadline you will have missed most of the scholarship deadlines.**

THE ESSAY IS A CRITICAL FACTOR

The essay can make or break an application. ANSWER THE PROMPT! Don't assume you can make one essay fit all applications. Your essay should be a narrative, telling an interesting story, revealing to the reader something about you not already found in the application. Humor is good, but above all, be genuine. Remember that the hardworking people in admissions offices have to read hundreds, sometimes thousands, of essays in a year, so make yours interesting for them. You don't have to be hilarious or shocking, but you do have to be engaging and sincere. The reader is not as interested in **what** happened to you, as in what the experience says about you or taught you.

Essays don't occur at one point in time, they evolve. A great essay usually takes a minimum of five or six edits. Read the six essay prompts on the Common Application. You only have to write on one prompt. Pick the story that best represents you. Check and recheck your essays to eliminate completely any spelling or grammatical errors. Having these errors in your essays says either "I'm ignorant" or "I don't care enough to be careful in material I'm submitting to you." Do you think colleges want to admit either of those types of people?

THE MOST COMMON APPLICATION MISTAKES
- Not answering the question. READ CAREFULLY!
- Misspelled words
- Grammar
- Failure to "SAVE" before moving on to the next page
- Push "SUBMIT" once you are completely satisfied with your application.
(Yes, a common mistake – many students think they have submitted when they have completed the application; it is not SUBMITTED until you press SUBMIT!)

RESTRICTED & UNRESTRICTED ADMISSION POLICIES

UNRESTRICTED	*RESTRICTED*
Rolling	Early Action Single Choice
Regular Decision	Restricted Early Action
Early Action	Early Decision

You may apply to as many "Unrestricted" schools as you wish without obligation to attend. You may apply to only ONE "Restricted" school and if accepted, you are expected to attend that school and withdraw all other applications.

NOTIFICATE DATE – Some colleges post a notification date for all applicants. This application can be submitted anytime from early fall until the submission date deadline. This means OPEN SEASON for your application. All applications will be processed and there will be a NOTIFICATION DATE when all applicants will learn the status of their application. Even if you are applying to a NOTIFICATION DATE college, it is a good idea to submit your application in the early fall when the "reader" will review your application in a short stack of applications rather than a tall stack. Also, you will not miss any scholarship deadlines if you submit in the early fall.

ROLLING – Usually from September on, you submit an application and about three to six weeks later the school will send you an admission decision letter. This type of school starts out its admission season with all seats in its freshman class open. As the school hands out more and more acceptances as the year proceeds, fewer places are left available and, at some point, all places are filled. It is, therefore, to your advantage to apply to rolling admissions schools as soon after September 1st as possible.

After making your campus visits, if one school is **THE TOP – NUMBER ONE** on your list, you might want to think about applying on their "Early" option. While the "EARLY" terms look and sound similar, they are different LEGALLY. The university will determine if the procedure is Early Action, Early Action Single Choice, Restricted Early Action or Early Decision.

EARLY ACTION – Many schools have this option. If you apply for Early Action, you are declaring to the university that you have submitted all of your forms by the required "Early" deadline and you are seriously considering attending the school. You may apply to more than one school through "Early Action."

RESTRICTED EARLY ACTION (EARLY ACTION SINGLE CHOICE) – Only a few schools have this option. You are declaring to the university that you have submitted all of the forms by the required "Early" deadline and that you are ONLY applying to one school, their school, through any kind of early program.

EARLY DECISION – Many schools have this option. "Early Decision" is a legal binding contract. If your college is an "Early Decision" school and you declare "Early Decision" rather than "Regular Decision" you are saying, **"I pick you…if you pick me…I'm coming!"** Schools are interested in Early Decision candidates because those students have expressed their interest in that particular college by committing ahead of time to attend if accepted. Students may be interested in Early Decision programs because a positive admission decision means that their college application process is completed, well, early! **YOU ARE REQUIRED TO ONLY APPLY TO ONE INSTITUTION AS AN "EARLY DECISION" CANDIDATE.** Take this step very seriously and make it work to your advantage when you really do have a clear first choice.

Note that when you apply under any of the early programs, colleges commit to giving you a decision by a certain date. This decision can take three forms:

1) Yes! You're Accepted! which may or may not mean that your process stops there, depending on whether you applied Early Action or Early Decision
2) No, we're sorry but you need to look elsewhere
3) Deferred - we're not saying yes or no for now, but will reconsider your application during our Regular Decision time.

Do you have one college as your very top choice? _____

Which one? _____

Is the policy of the school Rolling, Early Action, Early Action Single Choice or Early Decision? _____

Let's take a look at your top five to ten colleges.

What is the admission policy for each school?

UNIVERSITY	Rolling / Early Action Early Action Single Choice Early Decision
1.	
2.	
3.	
4.	
5.	
6.	
7.	
8.	
9.	
10.	

 ## MAGIC BULLET DATE = OCTOBER 1st

You will be amazed at how smooth the process will go if you try to have everything sent electronically or mailed to the colleges by October 1st. The admission cycle is young and exciting to the representatives as they anticipate the new crop of applicants. Just one month later because of "Early" plans due on the first of November, the daily stack of applications triples for the reader.

Would you rather have your application read on a day when the admissions officer is reading 25 other applications or on a day when the reader has 75 applications to read?

You can submit an application by October 1st without declaring "early" anything. It's just there – a regular application arriving early in the office of admission…**how impressive!**

LETTERS OF RECOMMENDATION

- When you ask teachers, or anyone for that matter to complete a letter of recommendation on your behalf, it is a good idea to supply them with a copy of your resume so they can write knowledgeably about you.

- Meet face to face with the person you ask to write a letter of recommendation and bring a copy of your resume to that meeting.

- DO NOT PUT REQUESTS IN TEACHER BOXES OR SEND REQUESTS TO THE WRITER WITHOUT ASKING FIRST! Such behavior is rude and presumptuous, and might result in a letter which is not in your best interest.

- Allow a **MINIMUM** of 10 working days for any recommendation to be processed from a teacher as well as school reports and transcripts from the guidance office. Depending on your school policy, provide an addressed stamped envelope to each writer for each college or ask them to place the recommendation on file in the counselor's office. Politely check back with the writer or your counselor **before** the deadline date to verify that your letter was mailed.

- For Home School students, your parents can process your school report but you should still respect the 10 day rule for your letter writers. Home School students, try to ask a writer who can speak about your academic achievement.

- **Follow-up with a "thank you" note to the person writing the recommendation.** Teachers and other writers are not required to write letters for you. It is their service to you. Remember to be appreciative. You may even be pro-active and attach the "thank you" note to the forms and resume before giving it to the teacher. If you really want to go the extra mile, consider enclosing a small gift card to a coffee shop or restaurant. After all, the person writing your letter of recommendation is giving up personal time above and beyond the school day or work day to help you get into college.

Follow Directions for Each College Application!

By the end of your junior year, you should have a general idea of the application procedures and requirements for each school. **Carefully follow the directions for each college.** Some schools will require specific teachers, such as English and math, to write letters while others will offer you a choice. Most colleges will want you to use only academic subject teachers (not fine arts, electives, or sports) from your junior or senior year for teacher recommendations. These teachers know you as a student of academic work closer to the college level.

Always be polite in every communication with EVERYONE at the college.

USEFUL COLLEGE PLANNING WEB SITES

Fast Web	**College Board**	**Financial Aid**
www.fastweb.com	www.collegeboard.com	www.fafsa.gov

UNIVERSITY HOME PAGES

To search for a specific college: All college home pages will end in ".edu". You can try the college name or acronym followed by ".edu". For example:

Boston College	www.bc.edu
Baylor University	www.baylor.edu
University of Missouri	www.missouri.edu

MAY 1st NOTIFICATION

If you have applied to a school and been accepted under an Early Decision program, you will have confirmed your commitment to the school at that time. Otherwise, if you are accepted under a Rolling Admissions, Regular Decision or an Early Action plan, no matter when you received your acceptance letter, colleges have agreed as a group that you do not have to let them know of YOUR decision until May 1. Failure to notify the college by May 1st could cost you your acceptance spot in the entering class. Make sure you reserve your place in the entering class.

" I may not be there yet but I'm closer than I was yesterday." ~ Author Unknown

People who write down their goals are more likely to achieve them! Make a list of the things you need to do to move this application train on down the track!

1. _____

2. _____

3. _____

4. _____

NOTE: In the final admission decision, if you are waitlisted at a school and you wish to move off the waitlist and gain admission follow these steps:

1. Write a cover letter to the university stating the school is still your top choice and you wish to move from "wait list" to "ADMIT!"

2. Send an undated resume highlighting the additions to your resume.

3. Send 3 to 5 samples of your work to provide evidence of your ability to successfully complete college level work. Examples of work might include an English research paper or lab reports from and AP science class – something that demonstrates your work level to be worthy of their attention.

"Nothing in this world can take the place of persistence. Talent will not; nothing is more common than unsuccessful people with talent. Genius will not; unrewarded genius is almost a proverb. Education will not; the world is full of educated derelicts. Persistence and determination alone are omnipotent. The slogan "press on" has solved and always will solve the problems of the human race."   *~ Calvin Coolidge*

"It is hard to fail but it is worse never to have tried to succeed" . ~ Theodore Roosevelt

Stay focused - Stay organized. Keep your notes together!

SECTION FOUR

-

PAYING FOR COLLEGE

SECTION FOUR - PAYING FOR COLLEGE
SCHOLARSHIPS AND FINANCIAL AID

Many students begin their college process thinking in terms of affordability first, then admission to a particular college. It's actually the other way around. **Never** avoid applying to a particular school because you believe you will not be able to afford it. You will <u>never</u> <u>know</u> unless you apply, are accepted, and then see how much assistance they are willing to give you. Submit your applications and then make contact with the Scholarship Office and Financial Aid Office at each school where you have applied. The college will ALWAYS be your PRIMARY source for scholarship and financial aid money. Students and parents often refer to scholarships and financial aid as one. Both are usually administered out of the same office and this can be confusing because it's like having apples and oranges in the same crate, so let's separate the crates!

SCHOLARSHIPS (the Apples)

Scholarships are based on merit. A scholarship is awarded in honor of achievement. Most scholarships require a class rank in the top 25% of the class. **ALL LEGITIMATE SCHOLARSHIPS ARE GIVEN AWAY.** Beware of multiple scams stating that thousands of dollars in scholarship money go unclaimed. No legitimate scholarship or scholarship service will require you to pay anything. **DO N OT EVER PAY ANYTHING TO ANY COMPANY WHO PROMISES SCHOLARSHIP OPPORTUNITIES. IF IT IS LEGITIMATE, IT IS FREE.**

Your best source of scholarship $$$ will come from the college or university where you apply. Translation: **APPLY EARLY!** The DEADLINE for scholarship applications usually falls long BEFORE the deadline for admission. The scholarship consideration deadline usually runs between November 1 and December 15. Check each college for their respective deadline dates. When the scholarship is awarded, the money is gone! If you follow the advice to submit everything for admission by October 1st, you will have plenty of time to turn your focus to scholarship opportunities. Remember, you are working with **FOUR** offices on each college campus:

1) Admission
2) Scholarship
3) Financial Aid
4) Housing

Typically, you may not be able to work with #2, #3 and #4 until your application is complete and on file at the university.

The application process can be exhausting, but you're almost there...don't give up now! Finding scholarships means making contacts with both private foundations and university scholarship offices. The college will always be your primary source of scholarship; private foundations and organizations will be your best secondary source. For secondary source scholarships register with www.fastweb.com and check with your guidance counselor.

PRIMARY SOURCES: List the schools where you have applied. Use the college website to find the phone number of the scholarship office. STUDENTS make the call! Call each college scholarship office and find out if there are any scholarships you might be considered for and ask whether there are any additional applications (forms) you need to complete for scholarships. Some schools simply use the admissions application and supplement to consider students for scholarships. Note: sometimes there is a box on the application where a student indicates that he/she would like to be considered for scholarship opportunities. Develop a "phone" relationship with a person in the scholarship office and always ask to speak to the same person.

COLLEGE APPLICATIONS ARE COMPLETE AT (list the college or university)	SCHOLARSHIP OFFICE PHONE NUMBER NAME OF CONTACT

It's not that I'm so smart it's just that I stay with problems longer!
~Albert Einstein

54

SCHOLARSHIP SOURCES

Many schools use merit-based scholarships as recruitment discounts for solid students. CHECK WITH EACH COLLEGE WHEN YOU SUBMIT AN APPLICATION. ALWAYS ASK THE COLLEGE SCHOLARSHIP OFFICE IF THERE ARE ADDITIONAL APPLICATION FORMS TO BE CONSIDERED FOR SCHOLARSHIP.

For specific majors go to google.com and enter the field of study + scholarships. For example: "engineering + scholarships" or "nursing + scholarships".

Academic scholarship awards typically require a strong SAT or ACT score, class rank in the top 25%, volunteer work and depth in activities. There are also scholarships for outstanding community service participation.

PRIMARY AND SECONDARY SOURCE SCHOLARSHIPS

Your best source of scholarship will be the college that you ultimately attend. It may be necessary to apply for scholarships at several different institutions before making a final decision on which school to attend. The college will always be your **PRIMARY** source for scholarship.

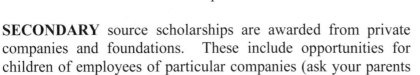

SECONDARY source scholarships are awarded from private companies and foundations. These include opportunities for children of employees of particular companies (ask your parents to check with the Human Resource Department at their companies), memberships in clubs and community organizations such as Rotary, credit unions and coops. Some states also offer scholarship incentives for the best and brightest.

SCHOLARSHIP SEARCH

Fastweb – www.fastweb.com
Coca-Cola Scholars – www.coca-colascholars.org
Sam Walton Community Scholarship – www.walmartfoundation.org
Arts Recognition and Talent Search – www.artsawards.org
Scholastic Art and Writing Awards – www.scholastic.com/artandwriting
Ayn Rand Institute Essay Competition – www.aynrand.org/contests
Public Speaking – www.legion.org and www.vfw.org
College Board – www.collegeboard.com/student/pay/index.html
Hispanic - www.hispanicheritageawards.org
Sallie Mae - www.salliemae.com
Scholarship for Minorities - www.blackexcel.org/200-Scholarships.html

FINANCIAL AID (the Oranges)

Financial Aid is based not on merit but on need. The colleges, therefore, will ask for evidence of that need. You must file a FAFSA (Free Application for Federal Student Aid) after January 1, of your senior year in order to be considered for Financial Aid. This is a lengthy process, so have your tax return ready to go! The forms say that you can estimate your tax information, but experience has proven estimating only slows down the process. Filing early is important! Once the grant money is given away, it's gone! Typically colleges start developing the individual financial aid packages around the first of April. Check with each of your colleges to determine the absolute best date to have all forms to each financial aid office.

Some private colleges will additionally ask you to fill out the CSS Profile which can be found at www.collegeboard.com . This form is very similar to the FAFSA and can be completed quickly using most of the same information. It is simply an additional tool for some colleges to use to make their assessment of your financial need. The CSS Profile can be completed in the fall of your senior year whereas the FAFSA must be filed AFTER January 1st of your senior year.

Financial Aid comes in several forms:

1) Federal Pell Grant
2) Federal Supplemental Grant
3) Federal Work-Study
4) Federal Perkins Loan
5) Federal Stafford Loan
6) Federal Plus Loans for Parents

Grants do not have to be repaid. Loans involve repayment. Work study can actually be a good thing. Students often find a close working relationship with their assigned department professor(s).

Once your FAFSA is on file at the college financial aid office at each university you are considering to attend, the Financial Aid Officer will evaluate it and notify you about programs for which you qualify. Typically, your financial aid package will include some grant, some work study, and some loans.

For FAFSA, make certain you use the www.fafsa.gov web site. There is a FAFSA.com site that will gladly charge you a substantial fee to fill out the **FREE** form at www.fafsa.gov! Remember, the first "F" in FAFSA stands for **FREE**!

Financial Aid Terminology

Pell Grant – Financial assistance funded by the federal government on the basis of need and designed to provide aid to those with severe need.

Federal Perkins Loan – loans funded by the federal government and awarded by the institution (the college). These loans have a low interest rate and are repayable over an extended period of time.

Guaranteed Student Loan – is subsidized by the government and does not incur interest until the student has been out of college for six months.

Unsubsidized Student Loan – interest begins incurring from the loan origin date.

Important Financial Aid Website

http://www.fafsa.gov

Getting Ready For The FAFSA

If you are completing the FAFSA online, you will need to apply for a PIN (personal identification number). You apply for a PIN at www.fafsagov.

Get organized. Parents (and students – if the student has worked and earned income) if you are ever going to be ready to go with your taxes make it the year to first apply for financial aid. You may apply AFTER January 1 of the senior year. However, many people will not have their taxes ready to file before late February or early March. While you can estimate, this often just slows down the process. The colleges will say "well this is very nice…now send us the accurate FAFSA data once you have filed your taxes. The money gets given away early – March and April – and when the money is gone…it's gone!

Finally, double check you have all the necessary information including electronic signatures on the form.

For specific questions about financial aid, there is a Federal student Aid Information Center (1-800-4-FED-AID).

"Diligence is the mother of good luck!" ~ Benjamin Franklin

Stay focused - Stay organized. Keep your notes together!

SECTION FIVE

-

SPECIAL PROGRAMS

SECTION FIVE
SPECIAL PROGRAMS

MILITARY SERVICE ACADEMIES

If you are interested in one of the military service academies, you should contact the academy **NO LATER THAN JANUARY OF YOUR JUNIOR YEAR.**

Several tasks must be accomplished simultaneously:

1. Contact the academy to complete the Pre-Candidate information form

2. Request a nomination to a military academy from your United States Congressman and Senators.

    Contact the U.S. Senators for your state at www.senate.gov
    Contact your Congressman using the web site www.house.gov

Many Congressmen have their academy applications available online. Once you complete the application, return it to the local office indicated on the forms, and try to become familiar with the local office personnel responsible for academy applications and decisions for your Congressman and Senators.

THE PROCESS FOR MILITARY ACADEMIES

An appointment to a United States Military Academy - West Point, Air Force, Navy, Coast Guard, or Merchant Marines is considered to be a $300,000+ scholarship. It takes a strong desire to serve your country. The application process is tedious and life as a cadet is rigorous, but the educational opportunity is without limits for the right applicant! Make contact with the academies no later than your junior year. The academy will then assign you a Liaison Officer for your school. This person will be a great resource for you as you go through the process outlined below:

Sophomore and Junior Year

1) Contact the academy and ask them to put you in contact with your Liaison Officer.

2) Make sure your guidance counselor, or parent if you are home schooled, knows about your interest in the academy.

Junior Year

1) Make sure you take and perform well on the PSAT.

2) Ask your Liaison Officer to help you apply for the special summer program at the academy. Admission to the summer program is by invitation ONLY and is based on PSAT.

3) Apply for a nomination through your Congressman and Senators.

4) Take the SAT Reasoning Test (formerly SAT I) and/or ACT.

Summer Before Senior Year

1) Take medical and physical aptitude tests as directed by the academy.

2) Complete the application to the academy.

3) Complete the applications to the Congressman and Senators.

ACADEMY CONTACT INFORMATION

Air Force
www.usafa.af.mil
1-800-443-9266

West Point
www.usma.edu
1-845-938-4041

Navy
www.usna.edu
1-410-293-4361

Coast Guard
www.cga.edu
1-877-883-8724

Merchant Marine
www.usmma.edu
1-516-773-5391

ROTC

The Reserve Officer Training Corps (ROTC) is another option for students interested in serving in the military. ROTC offers a wonderful way to have your education paid for with guaranteed occupations waiting for you after graduation. Seventy-five percent of all military officers come through the ROTC program. There are four-year and three-year scholarships with obligation to serve after graduation. Applying early (summer before senior year) gives you the edge!

Qualifications for ROTC scholarships include:

- age 17 – 27; single with no dependents
- top 10-15% of your class
- 28 ACT or 1300 SAT (critical reading and math)
- excellent physical condition.

ROTC students may attend any college that accepts ROTC scholarships. They may even attend one college for class and take their ROTC classes at a different nearby college. For information on ROTC scholarships, contact the following:

ROTC (Army)
1-800-USA-ROTC
www.armyrotc.com

AFROTC (Air Force)
1-800-522-0033
www.afrotc.com

NROTC (Navy, includes Marine Option)
1-800-NAV-ROTC
www.navy.com/careers/nrotc

NOTE: There is a six year commitment to attending a military academy or accepting an ROTC scholarship. It usually involves four years of active duty and two years of reserve duty. Again, this program is not for everyone but for those who have a desire to serve their country, ROTC provides incredible opportunities for scholarship and leadership.

<u>ATHLETES</u>

You must register with the NCAA Clearinghouse if you plan to participate in intercollegiate sports at college. You can review the eligibility requirements and register online.

For more information, you can visit the NCAA Clearinghouse website at:

www.ncaa.org

It is also recommended that students register with the National Association of Intercollegiate Athletics.

www.naia.org

Some athletes work with a recruiter. However, with or without a recruiter, realize **YOU** must be proactive and market yourself to the college coaches. Many college coaches say that they would prefer to hear from the athlete him/herself because it shows a pro-active attitude and that the student is particularly interested in that college. You will need an athletic resume representative of your athletic accomplishments. This would include timings, athletic achievements such as district and state honors, and participation in select teams. The following websites may help you.

Additional Resources for Athletes

Univ. Sports Programs: http://www.universitysports.com/

At the end of the season your junior year start sending your athletic resumes and DVD highlights to the college coaches at colleges you would like to attend. BE AGGRESSIVE – don't wait for them to contact you! If you don't know the name of the coach, call the school and ask for the athletic department. They can give you the name and campus address for the coach. Do not just send information to the athletic office. Make sure you are sending your information to the right person <u>by name</u>. **The coaches can then officially contact you AFTER you have completed the sport your junior year.** You must be registered with the NCAA to make an official athletic campus visit.

Athletes …Here's how the recruiting process works

1) Make sure you register with the NCAA Clearinghouse after you have finished the sport your junior year. www.ncaa.org

2) Sign a release form in the counselor's office granting permission to send your transcript to any coach who requests it.

Athletes...

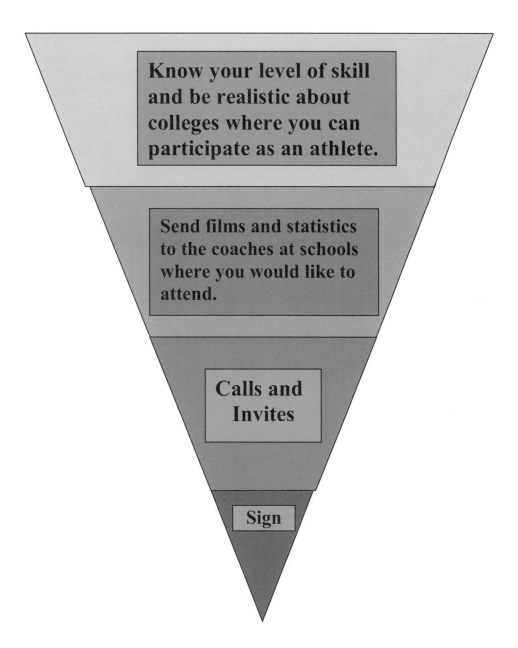

Know your level of skill and be realistic about colleges where you can participate as an athlete.

Send films and statistics to the coaches at schools where you would like to attend.

Calls and Invites

Sign

It's all about marketing yourself into the position you want. **YOU** must be aggressive! Begin your market campaign after you have finished the sport your junior year. Coaches will be calling 10-20 athletes for every position...they only need one athlete to "sign" (commit) for each position! Be aggressive and if an offer is made you want to accept, jump on it – do not hold out to see if something better comes along.

PERFORMING AND VISUAL ARTISTS

Much like the athletes, performing and visual artists will need to communicate with the departments at their respective campuses. You should also have a specific resume or portfolio to showcase your talent. As a performing artists you will in all likelihood <u>need to audition</u> or <u>present a portfolio</u>.

Begin communicating with colleges no later than your junior year to learn their schedules and timetables for audition and portfolio requirements. Be sure to check with **ALL** colleges on your list as portfolio requirements and audition requirements will vary from school to school.

For current information on local performing arts fairs, check with your colleges to learn about traveling audition dates and portfolio review in your area. National Portfolio Day brings together experienced college representatives to review work and offer critique. NPD also offers a forum for the exchange of information regarding work, college plans, and career plans. For more information visit the following website:

http://www.portfolioday.net/

Thespians please check with **ALL** of your colleges to determine respective audition times, places, and requirements. Request your audition slot early in the process as these times fill up. You will often be required to perform different genres. Prepare early!

DVDs, Portfolios & YOUTUBE

A word about DVDs, collages, portfolios and YOUTUBE…take the TIME to fully develop any supporting documentation you provide to colleges. It should be an example of your **VERY BEST** work. Creating an audition DVD, YOUTUBE or portfolio should take weeks not something put together overnight.

Always contact each college where you plan to apply to determine audition/portfolio requirements and dates.

COLLEGE PLANNING TIMELINE

COLLEGE TIMELINE

Fall of the 9th Grade	Take a strong curriculum and do your best to make good grades. One day a college admissions officer will actually look at your transcript (your grades) and make a decision on your work ethic based on your grades. If college representatives visit your school, take time to visit with them and ask them about things of interest to you. Get involved in one or two school activities such as sports, music, theatre, debate, newspaper, etc., and keep that involvement throughout all four years of high school. If your school allows 9th graders to take the PSAT and PLAN, by all means do so. Practice leads to perfection! Think about getting some in depth involvement in community service. While four or five hours here and there are better than nothing, look for volunteer activities where you want to make a long term commitment.
Spring of 9th Grade	Continue to work hard on your grades. Preparation today will avoid last minute panic. Continue your activities and your community service work. Think about taking a summer enhancement program at a local college. Almost every college in the country offers some type of program for high school students. This is a great way to get on campus and investigate colleges.
Fall of 10th Grade	Take the PSAT as practice and the PLAN (preliminary ACT). Check with your school counselor early in September to see if you need to register and pay a fee for these exams. Home school students may test at their public school or private schools. Reserve your test early as materials are ordered over the summer prior to the test. Attend your College Fair with a list of colleges you want to see and a set of questions you want to ask (see page 17). Visit with college representatives who visit your school. Keep up your grades, activities and volunteer service.
Spring of 10th Grade	Know your range of SAT and ACT scores through your PSAT and PLAN results, it is appropriate for you to make some campus visits in

	the spring of your sophomore year. To visit with a purpose, make each visit with a set of questions you want to have answered. COLLEGE VISIT TEMPLATE for campus visits (see pages 25)! Keep up your grades and activities. Make arrangements to take a formal SAT / ACT prep class this summer. Check with your Guidance Counselor to see what prep programs in your area deliver the best results. Make plans to take a summer enhancement course at a college of interest to you. Almost every college offers a summer program for high school students. This is a great way to "try out" a college on your list.
Summer after 10th Grade	**PREP FOR THE PSAT!** This is a MUST! You wouldn't expect the football team to play a game without practice or to play a piano performance without practicing, don't take this important exam without practicing! Think of a PSAT Prep Class as organized practice for one of the most important exams of your high school career (see pages 3-4).
Fall of 11th Grade	Fall of Junior Year - Check with your counselor to make sure you are registered to take the PSAT in October. Home School students reserve your place for testing. The PSAT in your junior year is the ONLY test that qualifies you to become a National Merit Scholar. BE PREPARED! THIS IS ONE TEST, GIVEN ONLY ON ONE DAY TO BE NAMED NATIONAL MERIT! Attend your fall college fair and speak with EVERY college representative who visits your school. You might discover a new college for your consideration list. Grades are especially important in the junior year…this is the last set of grades a college will see before making an admission decision on you.
11th Grade	Check your calendar and make Campus Visits throughout the year. Register and take two SATs and two ACTs (see page 8). These exams are only given six or seven times a year so check your school and personal calendar and register early. It is your responsibility to know if your colleges require SAT Subject Tests. The SAT Subject Tests (formerly SAT II) tests are given on the same day as the SAT Reasoning Test (SAT I) so plan carefully! Keep the momentum going after the PSAT! It's recommended to begin taking the SAT in January of the junior year.

	If you're an athlete, you need to register with the NCAA, then you can begin the recruiting process after you have finished the sport your junior year (see pages 63-65). If you're a musician, thespian or visual artist, contact your colleges and make sure you know the requirements and deadlines for portfolios, audition tapes, and audition opportunities in your local area (see page 66).
Spring of 11th Grade	Take the SAT and ACT exams. Take the AP® exams offered for your respective AP courses. You will need to register for these with your school counselor. Home School students may take the AP Exams at public or nearby private schools. The exams must be ordered in March! Provide your chosen junior teachers with the recommendation forms from the Common Application and a copy of your resume. Do this while the teachers have a clear memory of you, your work habits and your class participation (see page 47).
Summer Before 12th Grade	Your grade point average is set and you should be finished with the SAT and ACT Exams. Narrow down your college choices and decide where you will send applications. Make campus visits. Work on your applications...INCLUDING THE ESSAYS (see pages 41-44)! Some schools will offer summer seminar type programs to help you complete your applications. By all means, try to attend such a program when possible – it will save you much grief and take the "nag" away from your parents. Both you and your parents will then be freed up to enjoy your senior year without the stress of college applications.
Fall of 12th Grade	Attend your college fair program and finalize your list of colleges. Visit with college representatives who visit your school from the colleges where you plan to apply. Last chance to secure recommendations! Realizing that teachers are not required to write letters on your behalf, remember to send the teacher a thank you note for writing your letters...and chocolate is always nice too! In other words, go the extra mile!

October 1 Senior Year	**ALL** applications in the mail by October 1. If you are applying for Rolling Admission, Regular Decision, Early Action, Early Decision, Restricted Early Action or Early Action Single Choice, it doesn't matter. **SEND ALL applications by October 1.** Make this a goal and you will qualify for more many more scholarship and leadership programs. And have a much less stressful senior year! (See page 47).
December of 12th Grade	Send additional follow-up information to your colleges to keep your name in front of them! It might be an updated resume, a copy of an especially good graded essay, or research paper (with teacher comments and all!).
Spring of 12th Grade	Take the AP® exams offered for your respective AP courses. You will need to register for these with your school counselor. If you're a Home School student you will need to make arrangements at a public or nearby private school no later than March 1 to take these exams.
May 1 12th Grade	**Notify all of the colleges where you were accepted that you are either accepting or declining their offer.** It's amazing, but some students forget to do this! (See page 48). Colleges will give your spot away if you have not confirmed with them your plans to attend.
After Graduation	Request a final transcript sent to the college you plan to attend.

If you will follow this timetable, you will swiftly navigate your road to college and avoid the potholes along the way. Make the process work FOR YOU! Safe travel!

The only time you must not fail is the last time you try. ~Charles F. Kettering

Stay focused - Stay organized. Keep your notes together!

_____

_____

_____

_____

_____

_____

_____

_____

_____

_____

_____

_____

_____

_____

_____

_____

_____

Stay focused - Stay organized. Keep your notes together!

Stay focused - Stay organized. Keep your notes together!

Stay focused - Stay organized. Keep your notes together!

Stay focused - Stay organized. Keep your notes together!

Stay focused - Stay organized. Keep your notes together!